Buzzy and the Little Critters

A Curious Tale of a Cicada Invasion

written and illustrated by

Kenton R. Hill

LUMINARE PRESS

WWW.LUMINAREPRESS.COM

Buzzy and the Little Critters
A Curious Tale of a Cicada Invasion

Written and illustrated by Kenton R. Hill © 2016

Printed in the United States of America

Cover Design by Claire Flint Last
Author Photo by Ed Keene

Luminare Press
467 W 17th Ave
Eugene, OR 97401

www.luminarepress.com

ISBN: 978-1-944733-10-0

*To my mother, who was the first to read to me
and who taught me how to read.*

*To my father, an entomologist, who taught me
to love bugs and shared the fun of drawing.*

"No. Don't!" Boone yelled. But, it was too late. Rosa had just stomped down hard. Crushing the big black bug.

When Boone asked his friend, "Why did you do that?" Rosa said, "It was an accident. But, what do you care? It's just a creepy bug."

"It is *not* creepy. It's cool, and it's harmless!" Boone shouted back.

"What's the big deal?" Rosa replied. "There are millions of them flying all around, and they won't stop making that loud, buzzing noise." Rosa went on screeching, "Weeee-ah, WEEEE-AH, weeee-ah, WEEEE-AH!"

1

Boone had to agree about the buzzing. It was July, and their town had just been invaded by thousands and thousands of cicadas. They were flying everywhere and buzzing so loudly that Boone felt like he had to cover his ears to keep his head from exploding.

"Why do they have to do that? Why do they buzz all the time?" Rosa wondered.

Boone, who was also curious, replied, "I'm going to find out. I'll ask my grandpa. He knows everything about bugs. He's an entomologist."

"What is an entomologist?" asked Rosa.

"That's a fancy word for a scientist who studies insects," Boone proudly answered as he started off to see his grandpa. "You can come with me, if you promise to be careful and not step on any more cicadas along the way."

When they reached his grandpa's house, Boone couldn't wait to ask, "Grandpa, why do cicadas make that loud, buzzing sound?"

Boone's grandpa smiled his scientist smile and said, "It is just the nature of the little critters."

That didn't exactly answer their question. But, Boone's grandpa went on to tell them more. He told how the female cicadas lay their eggs in tree branches. Each one lays as many as 600 eggs.

In a month or so, the eggs hatch and drop from the tree branches as tiny baby cicadas called nymphs. The nymphs burrow down deep under ground, and live there for seventeen long years as they grow up.

Then, they crawl back out of the ground, climb up a tree, shed their shell, and become a grown-up cicada. For the next six weeks, they fly around, buzzing, and finding a mate, so more eggs can be laid in the tree branches before the adult cicadas die.

BOOK of BUGS

ROSCOE E. HILL

Boone's grandpa concluded by saying, "That is if they don't get eaten by other critters."

"Eaten by other critters?" Rosa asked in surprise.

"Oh no!" was Boone's response.

"Oh, yes!" Boone's grandpa went on, "There are many hungry critters underground, on the ground, in the trees, and up in the sky who love the taste of cicadas."

Boone and Rosa were also getting hungry. It was time to go. They each headed off, back to their homes with all they had heard bouncing around in their brains.

Boone had dinner and got ready for bed. After saying good night to his new pet lightning bug, Lyle, he couldn't stop thinking about what his grandpa had told him about the nature of cicadas and especially how many other critters are out to get them.

Boone tossed and turned, recalling how sad he was when Rosa stomped on the defenseless cicada and thinking about all of the enemies cicadas have to be worried about. Finally he fell asleep.

While Boone was sleeping, a magical thing was happening. In his dream he was changing from a boy to a bug. He was changing from Boone, the boy, to Buzzy, the cicada.

As the dream continued, Buzzy paused when he spotted a molehill. You would think a baby cicada nymph would be safe under the ground six feet deep, but that is not how it is.

When Buzzy heard the sound of a frightened nymph coming from below the ground, he knew there was trouble. He was sure a hungry mole was heading for the nymph.

Buzzy raced to the rescue!

Buzzy knew he needed help. So, he called on his buddy, Lyle, the lightning bug, and they dove into the nymph's underground tunnel. Lyle went first, lighting the way.

Just before the mole could chomp down on the nymph, Lyle turned his lighted backside toward the mole's face and flashed his best flashes. Buzzy flapped his wings wildly and made the loudest, most outrageous buzzing sound he could make.

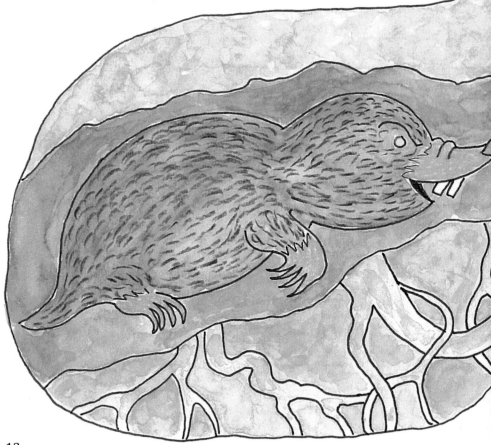

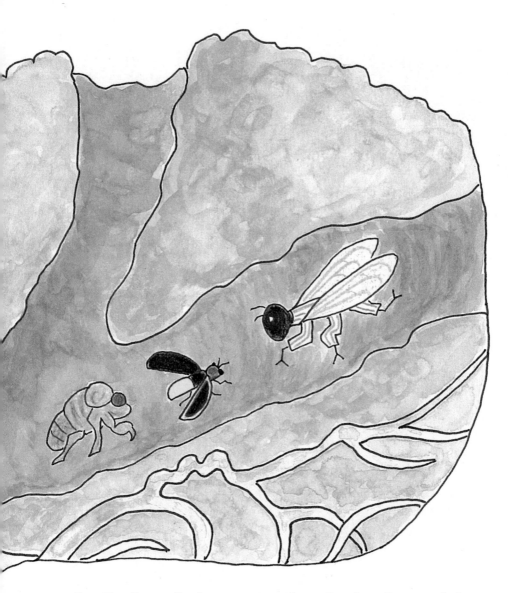

The flashing light was too bright for the mole's little eyes. And the buzzing was too loud for the mole's little ears. It backed up as fast and as far as its stubby legs would take it.

The nymph had been saved!

Back up above ground, Buzzy thanked Lyle. Knowing lightning bugs usually sleep during the day, Buzzy sent him back to his jar and looked around for further signs of trouble. And it didn't take long for trouble to arrive.

A creamy white cicada just coming out of its nymph's shell was in danger. It was hanging on the side of a tree, hoping to live to become a fully-grown black cicada.

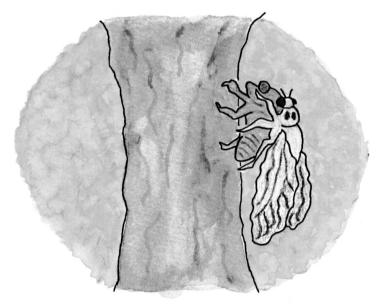

Perched high on the limb of a nearby tree was a blue jay. Its eyes were fixed on the young cicada, its beak half open, ready for its next meal. The bird spread its wings and dove at the cicada.

At the very last second, Buzzy took off as fast as he could fly, head first, straight toward the diving blue jay. He delivered a whopping head butt that sent the hungry bird off in the opposite direction.

It was Buzzy to the rescue for a second time!

After all of this action, Buzzy was tired and felt that a nap would be a good idea. However, he knew with all of those cicada enemy critters out there, he might be needed again. So, he decided to snooze lightly, just in case.

And sure enough, Buzzy was awakened by a faint humming sound.

Not as loud as a cicada…
Louder than a fly…
More like a bee…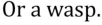
Or a wasp.
Yes, that's it…
…It was a wasp.

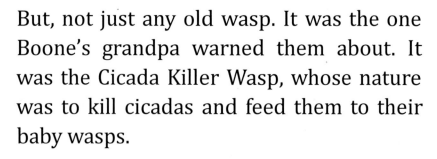

But, not just any old wasp. It was the one Boone's grandpa warned them about. It was the Cicada Killer Wasp, whose nature was to kill cicadas and feed them to their baby wasps.

As Buzzy woke to the humming sound, the killer wasp was heading right for him. It was Buzzy who was in danger this time. How was he going to save himself?

He needed to use his two greatest cicada powers to survive. And so he did.

Just before the killer wasp landed on top of Buzzy with its stinger ready, Buzzy let out his scariest buzz and took off flying. He used his buzzing on and off, loud and soft, to confuse the killer wasp.

He did every flying trick he could think of. Flying up and down. Flying back and forth. Then Buzzy did his best cicada trick—his spinning move. He flew faster and faster, around and around the killer wasp, until it got so dizzy it fell to the ground and staggered off into the bushes. Unable to fly. Unable to sting.

Buzzy had defended himself!

As the dream was ending, Buzzy stopped to think and to look around one more time at all of the trees, all of the cicadas, and all of the other critters. The hungry ones.

Boone woke up—rubbing the sleep from his eyes—remembering he was a boy not a bug.

After breakfast, Boone stopped by Rosa's house and together they hurried off to see his grandpa.

Boone told his grandpa and Rosa about his dream and how exciting it was to become a cicada and see all that his grandpa had told them about the lives and natures of this little critter. He saw how they get to dig around in the ground, sucking on roots—hanging out, getting ready to be all grown up. And as adults, how they have fun flying and singing their buzzing songs, distracting their enemies, and staying alive until it is their time to die.

Boone also told about how in his dream he was able to protect at least some of the cicadas.

Life Cycle of A Cicada

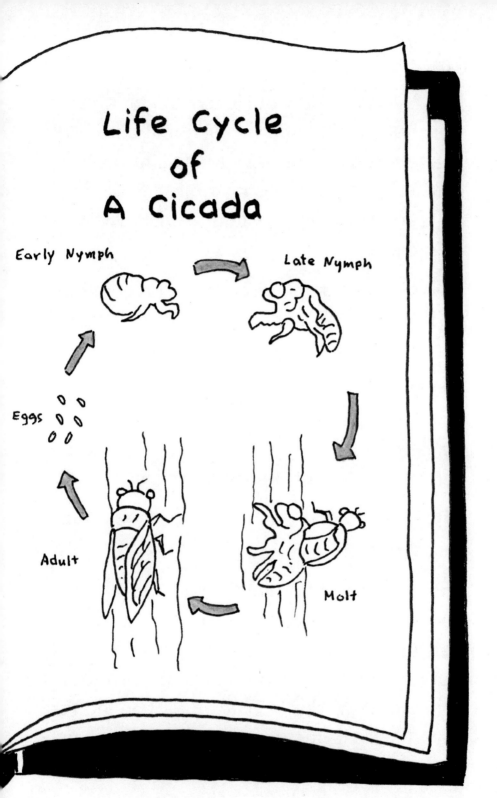

Early Nymph

Late Nymph

Eggs

Adult

Molt

"I had a dream too," Rosa added. "I didn't turn into a cicada, and I don't remember it very well, but I woke up thinking about all those hungry critters. And how they all have their own instincts and reasons to live. How they all have their own jobs to do—their own babies to feed."

Rosa's comment made Boone and his grandpa pause and think along with her. Think more about the nature of critters—all critters.

After a while Boone said, "Grandpa, I know we're not like those little critters, but now I am curious about my own nature. I am wondering what will happen with my life."

"Yes", Rosa was wondering too. "What will we become?"

Boone's grandpa liked what Rosa and Boone were thinking. He smiled his grandpa smile and said, "Well, we are different from those little critters. We all have our own natures, that's true. But, you don't have to settle for your instincts. You can choose. You can decide..."

Boone and Rosa smiled back at Boone's grandpa. And then at each other, as all sorts of possibilities began to pop into their heads…

"Grandpa, can you tell us more about these little critters?"

"Sure, here are a few
more fun facts..."

1. The word cicada means "buzzer" in Latin.

2. The preferred pronunciation is sih-KAY-duh.

3. Cicadas live in every country of the world except Antarctica (ant-ahrk-ti-kuh).

4. There are over 3,390 different species (spee-sheez) of cicadas in the world.

5. They range in size from 1 to 2 inches with wingspans of 5 to 8 inches.

6. They have 5 eyes—3 simple eyes to see light and dark, and 2 eyes to see the world around them.

7. Yearly cicadas, which come out every year in July and August are called "dog-day" cicadas.

8. Periodic (peer-ee-od-ik) cicadas are either on a 13 year cycle (si-kuhl) or a 17 year cycle.

9. The life cycle goes from egg (falling from the tree branch in 6 to 10 weeks), to nymph (nimf), who digs into the ground as deep as 8 feet, feeding on root juice (for 1, 13, or 17 years), to become an adult who lives 6 weeks at the most.

10. The nymphs crawl out of the ground at 64 degrees Fahrenheit (far-uhn-ha-hyt) over a week at the most.

11. There can be as many as 750,000 cicadas per acre.

12. The nymphs climb up a tree—always attaching themselves heads up as high as possible making room for the rest.

13. As they crawl out of their nymph shells they turn from white to black within 2 to 3 hours.

14. The males come out of the ground first (making it safer for the females).

15. The males are the only ones who make the buzzing sound.

16. They begin "singing" in a few days.

17. Their loud buzzing can reach 90+ decibels (des-uh-bel) about the same as a lawn mower.

18. Buzzing occurs in the heat of the day, and they rest at night.

19. They make their sound not by rubbing their legs together like a cricket, but by flexing their tymbals (tim-buhl), which are drum-like organs found in their abdomens (ab-duh-muhn).

20. One song is to confuse and distract predators (pred-uh-ter). Another is to attract a mate.

21. Forty percent of the cicadas are males. Sixty percent are females.

22. They suck fluid from plants mostly for water to keep from drying out and to keep cool during the hot summer days.

23. Female cicadas lay 10 to 30 eggs in each twig or branch, and up to 600 total per female.

24. Cicadas are not good at defending themselves, but outnumber the other critters in the area, who get their fill of early emerging males, leaving the rest to mate and trying their best to produce another generation of cicadas.

25. Every living thing has a positive reason for existing, even the mosquito.

"Grandpa, you said all critters have a positive reason-a positive purpose in life. What are cicadas good for?"

"There are many good things I can tell you..."

Cicadas have many admirable virtues:

- They don't use up valuable resources to survive—they sleep outside and don't need food—just dew and fresh air.

- They are dependable—great examples of showing up "on time".

- They are brave and will "take one" for the team.

- They have a great variety of buzzing songs.

- And, they are really good at flying up and down and all around.

Cicadas provide nutrition (food) to many other critters:

- Almost every creature on earth eats cicadas—from cats and dogs, to squirrels and raccoons, from owls and blue jays, to praying mantises and toads, even humans.

- Cicada Killer Wasps are especially fond of feeding cicadas to their baby wasps.

- When cicadas die they provide nutrients for the ground and trees.

Cicadas also serve mankind in special ways:

- They trim off old, weak branches as eggs are laid.

- They bring air into the ground as they climb out from their underground tunnels.

- They create a rare and memorable event.

- They inspire authors, artists and musicians.

- They are good for the economy by attracting tourists, vendors, and creating work for car washers.

- And they provide jobs for entomologists like me.

"When and where can I see the
17-year cicadas again, Grandpa?"

"There are twelve groups (broods) of periodic cicadas. Here is a list of the states and the years the 17-year cicadas will be buzzing again."

Brood	Year				General Region
I	2012	2029	2046	2063	VA, WV
II	2013	2030	2047	2064	CT, MD, NC, NJ, NY, PA, VA
III	2014	2031	2048	2065	IA, IL MO
IV	2015	2032	2049	2066	IA, KS, MO, NE, OK, TX
V	2016	2033	2050	2067	MD, OH, PA, VA, WV
VI	2017	2034	2051	2068	GA, NC, SC
VII	2018	2035	2052	2069	NY
VIII	2019	2036	2053	2070	OH, PA, WV
IX	2020	2037	2054	2071	NC, VA, WV

Brood	Year				General Region
X	2021	2038	2055	2072	DE, GA, IL, IN, KY, MD, MI, NC, NJ, NY, OH, PA, TN, VA, WV
XIII	2024	2041	2058	2075	IA, IL, IN, MI, WI
XIV	2025	2042	2059	2076	KY, GA, IN, MA, MD, NC, NJ, NY, OH, PA, TN, VA, WV

"And if you want to learn even more about cicadas, here are some ideas...."

Quick reference:

www.wikipedia.org/wiki/magicicada.

Active, up-to-date information on cicadas:

www.cicadamania.com.

A fun website for parents, teachers and bugdorks:

www.thebugchicks.com.
    The Bug Chicks are entomologists with a mission
    to change the way people think about insects,
    spiders and arthropods.

Other information sources for Boone's story
included the Department of Entomology at the
University of Nebraska and the following books:

Lang, Elliott and Wil Hershberger, 2007, *The Songs
    of Insects*, Boston, New York, Houghton Mifflin
    Company

Pringle, Laurence, 2010, *Cicadas! Strange and Won-
    derful,* Honesdale, Pennsylvania, Boyds Mills
    Press, Inc.

Roza, Greg, 2012, *The Bizarre Life of a Cicada*, New
    York, Gareth Stevens Publishing

Shian, Davy, 2008, *Cicada: Exotic Views,* Hebei Fine
    Arts Publishing House

42432715R00028

Made in the USA
San Bernardino, CA
03 December 2016